got mammo?

101 silver linings
of being a
breast cancer survivor!

"This book's a hoot—pun intended!"
Lillie Shockney, RN, BS, MAS
Johns Hopkins Avon Foundation Breast Center, Admin. Dir.

Wendi Lou Steele & Judge Cohen

got mammo?

101 silver linings of being a breast cancer survivor!

STAY PERKY!
Wendi Lou Steele

Wendi Lou Steele & Judge Cohen

First edition 2009

Library of Congress Catalog Card Number:
Steele, Wendi Lou
Summary: An illustrated laugh-out-loud gift book for breast cancer survivors.
ISBN: 978-0-615-25145-5

Interested in oodles of copies? Please see:
gotmammo?.com

Printed in the good ol' U.S.A.

"got mammo?"

Even aspiring to fill an ' A ' cup,
smashed like road kill your figure is voluptuous!

Receive more callbacks than an aspiring actress.

*Your boob now has more Kodak Moments
than a Hollywood starlet.*

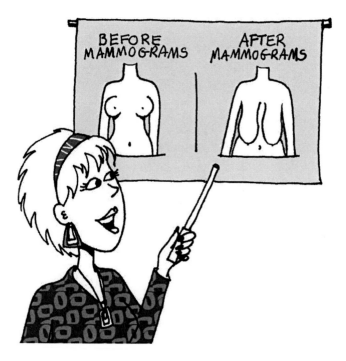

Win a Nobel Prize
for discovering why old broads' boobs sag.

After the biopsy,
find another use for Costco-sized bags of frozen peas.

After your chest deflates, hug your radiologist and thank her for saving your life.

Finally, you receive man's undivided attention.

Discover you have more support from your friends than you ever needed in your bra.

Still here! Every morning is magnificent.

Hire an agent
to manage the multiple demands on your time.

Going to a tanning salon is justified due to
all the folks who are scheduled to see you naked.

Moon your best friend.

BEFORE

AFTER

Design flattering, chic hospital gowns.

Be sure to get a manicure before your PET scan.

The intellectual elitists find you fascinating . . .

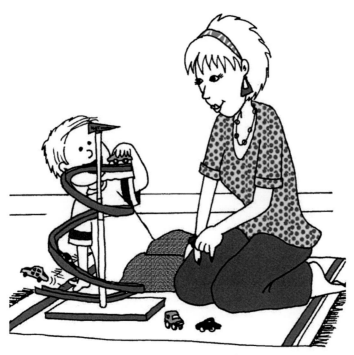

*even though playing Hot Wheels
hasn't been this much fun since you were five.*

Epiphany: The cost of your health insurance premium
is a bargain!

Need a mastectomy?
Consider it a weight loss plan.

Need a double?
Apply for *The Biggest Loser.*

Hospital stay? You finally control the remote!

Order breakfast in bed – and you don't have to
do the dishes, either.

Even if you voted for Ronald Reagan,
you can use narcotics 24/7 and no one will balk.

And if you voted for Bill Clinton,
no one will notice anyway.

Before you check out of the hospital,
give your flowers away to non-whiners
whose rooms need a makeover.

Lymph nodes clear?
Improv an Ellen DeGeneres dance with your surgeon.

Not clear? Pout for five minutes,
volunteer at the nearest Ronald McDonald House,
then improv an Ellen dance with the kids.

Redesign the children's hospital gowns
and donate all the proceeds.

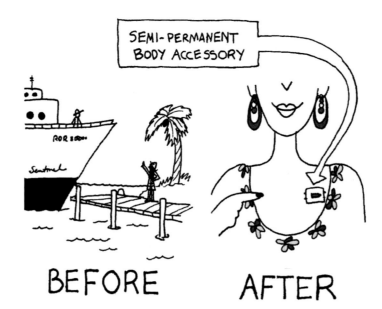

Discover how many people love you!

Now that you're bilingual, re-read your pathology report. However ironic, deem it a blessing to discover that you have "unremarkable nipples."

All the men you hang with nowadays
dig you for your mind and witty personality.

The President of The Gargantuan Greeting Card Company
sends you a personal thank you note
for boosting quarterly earnings.

After your surgery, doctors won't let you vacuum . . .

or drive the soccer or Little League car pools.

Legit excuse to never volunteer for squat!

Bring your own cucumber and polish –
a prescription for physical therapy
is the equivalent of trips to a day spa.

Receive unexpected compliments.

Designate which side's your good side because . . .

*everyone hugs you when you enter a room
and they all squeeze a tad longer.*

Allow friends to throw a Booby Bunko Party in your honor and take home all the cash for your future breast prosthesis.

Giggle yourself silly when your five-year-old announces,
" It grew back!"

Let your preteen daughter try it on.

Howl when your preschooler asks
if he can bring your boob in for Show and Share Day.

Reconstruction? Move over Pamela Anderson but beware of Borat from Kazakhstan.

You`ll have to say good-bye to The Biggest Loser . . .

but you'll be cast in another Baywatch sequel.

More prescriptions? Consider quest for a second Nobel
Prize for paper entitled: It's Not the Chemo that Makes
Patients Nauseous - It's the Price of the Meds.

Chemo freeing up your schedule?
Flaunt your activist side.

Read the classics . . .

or, perhaps not.

Catch up on your beauty sleep.

Enjoy getting loopy without a hangover.

"Martha" the oncologist's office.

Race fellow patients to the single bathroom.

Play tricks on the chemo nurse: swap out your drip de
jour for a pomegranate/vodka cocktail.

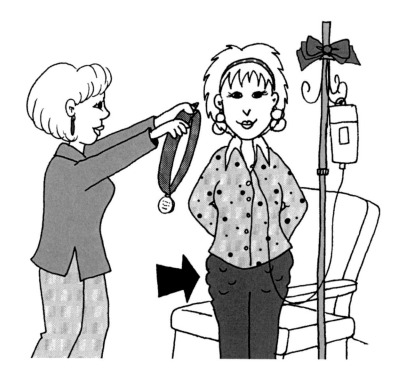

Wear a Depends pad for your next session and win the Bladder of Steel contest.

When your taste buds recover, upgrade from the House wine.

Your neighbors' casseroles are the new Food Pyramid.

Guilt free eating after 9:00 pm!

Sell pre-owned plastic Tupperware on eBay
and make $250,000.67 . . .

or open a ContainerMax dealership and become a publicly traded stock.

Chemo making you nauseous and feeling preggers with septuplets? At least you won't have to change a single diaper at 2:am . . .

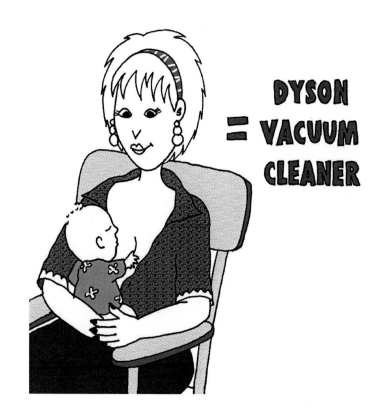

DYSON = VACUUM CLEANER

and you definitely won't have to nurse.

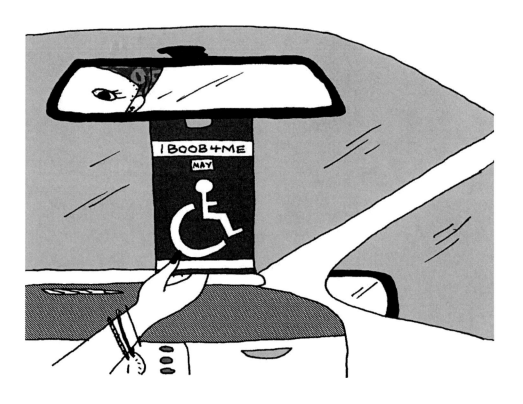

Let your parking angel take a leave of absence.

Shop on Christmas Eve
and still find a fab parking spot at the mall.

Be proactive: SHAVE!

Host a Brittany Wanna-Be Party.

Empower your daughter – Invite broads of all ages
to wear head cover-ups and, of course,

. . . to bring chocolate!

So you don't create an International Incident,
guests must deposit all lotions, gels, and creams
at the front door.

Wear a Dolly wig and huge silver hoops
and look hot no matter how you vote.

Or call it your G. I. Jane Enlistment Send-off.

Just make sure you shave before your friends imbibe too much.

Give awards to Most Likely to be Emulated
by Saturday Night Live . . .

Get gifts and cards and gift cards
without turning a year older.

Receive a second grateful letter from the President of The Gargantuan Greeting Card Company for single-handedly propelling the company to record sales.

After the party, allow your kids to eat chocolate for breakfast - just don't tell their teachers.

No more bad hair days . . . or gray hair days.

Don't rush touch-ups because when you miss sections, you resemble a Chinese Crested puppy.

For once, have perfect highlights and see
if blondes, indeed, have more fun.

Save oodles on salon bills.

Use that money to accessorize!

Buy scarves and flattering new clothes . . .

like a yellow jersey. Win the Tour de Burbs!

Wear glam hats like Princess Di.

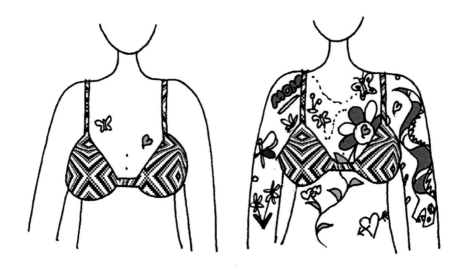

BEFORE   **AFTER**

Surprise your radiologist: embellish your boarder tattoos and appear on an episode of Your Town's Ink.

Women you've never met treat you like a sister.

Vacation whenever you can.

Wake up with a free, Brazilian bikini " wax" job . . .

without the razor burn!

Catch Nerf balls without using your hands.

Make sure your swim boob doesn't do a Nemo-escape
and drift off to Sydney.

But if it does, scream . . .

and have the water to yourself.

Or not –
but you don't sweat the small stuff anymore.

Shave until your kids go to college,
the neighbors will keep bringing you dinner.

Truly celebrate every birthday.

Open more cards, including one from the President of The Gargantuan Greeting Card Company offering you a place on their Board of Directors!

Politely decline the offer, citing too many fabulous places to go and things to do.

The ~~End~~ Beginning (again)

Author: Wendi Lou Steele

Appointments by Presidents Reagan, Bush (Daddy) and Clinton highlight my political career. Recently, "breast cancer survivor!" was added to my resume. I'm also mom to three munchkins, from whom I received much inspiration for this project. All my friends' generous gifts of chocolate still have them bouncing off the walls. Yikes.

Cartoonist: Judge Cohen

I try to keep the cats off the keyboard and the lid on the chaos. Published in all the Yippee-I've-Made-It markets, this project was a labor of love, definitely not money. Please buy lots & lots of copies so a Gargantuan Publishing Company signs our book! We thank you.

gotmammo.com